HIDDEN TREASURES

CARMARTHENSHIRE

Edited by Lucy Jeacock

FOREWORD

This year, the Young Writers' Hidden Treasures competition proudly presents a showcase of the best poetic talent from over 72,000 up-and-coming writers nationwide.

Young Writers was established in 1991 and we are still successful, even in today's technologically-led world, in promoting and encouraging the reading and writing of poetry.

The thought, effort, imagination and hard work put into each poem impressed us all, and once again, the task of selecting poems was a difficult one, but nevertheless, an enjoyable experience.

We hope you are as pleased as we are with the final selection and that you and your family continue to be entertained with *Hidden Treasures Carmarthenshire* for many years to come.

CONTENTS

Bigyn CP School

Ysgol Gynradd Cwmgors

The Poems

THE LAND OF THE ELVES

Deep in the mountains live the elves,
In the beautiful town of Delves.

In their cloaks of red and green,
In the dark they're never seen.

Dragons they slay
In a country so far away.

The elves go on adventures by night
And make tools and weapons in the light.

Amy Williams (10)
Bigyn CP School

THE MOUSE

There was a little mouse
Who lived in a house.
His name was Charlie,
His sister's name was Sally.

They lived in a tree
Which was beside the sea.
They had to be careful
Because of the big cat called Snowball.

They liked to eat cheese
And the mother told them always to say please.
They are furry mice,
Who like to look nice.

Elly Davies (11)
Bigyn CP School

WALES

Mountains as big as I've ever seen,
Beaches and coves, golden and clean,
Castles that rise up to the sky,
Some are knocked down, I don't know why.
I love living in Wales,
Except for the rain, snow and the gales.
People as friendly as you'll ever meet,
Wales is so good, it's hard to beat.

Kirsty Owen (10)
Bigyn CP School

My Best Friend!

My best friend is proper nice,
She's tons and tons of style.
A girly lass with bags of class
And a great big, smashing smile.

Every day we go to town
And buy our clothes and toys,
We always share our secrets,
Most of them are about boys.

We pile the make-up on our faces
And get ready to groove,
'Cause we're going to the disco
Where we really move.

My best friend means the world to me,
I think she's flipping brill,
Some say we'll drift apart,
But I know we never will.

Emma Gasser (11)
Bigyn CP School

TREASURED HOLIDAYS

Florida is the land of make-believe
Where Disney magic comes to breathe,
It finds its way among young and old,
Together they cherish the memories they hold.

Cyprus is hot, very, very hot,
Some fantastic memories I've still got,
From playing in the pool to seeing the sights,
Cyprus has some wonderful delights.

Rachel Evans (9)
Bigyn CP School

LAST NIGHT

When I looked out of my window last night,
I saw an amazingly wonderful sight.
I saw a lovely bright red glow
Coming from the grass below.

Fire flames burning, lovely and bright,
Woke me up in the middle of the night.
With its glow so bright and hot,
Will it come again? I think not.

Kayleigh Jones (9)
Bigyn CP School

THE HEADLESS HORSEMAN

It all started on a spooky night,
So we decided to have a fight.
Before we started kicking and punching,
We saw something that was jumping
Beneath the grass and the mud.
There it was, a jumping bug.
We tried to catch it
But it was too fast,
We decided to leave it alone,
But when we looked up, we couldn't find home.
On the track we had a treasure map
Which showed the way back to a golden sack.
We shared it carefully between us all,
And never told anyone at all.

Yousif Suliman (11)
Bigyn CP School

THE CAT

I have a furry cat,
He likes to sit on the mat.
He has very long claws
At the end of his paws.
He climbs up the trees
To play with the leaves,
Then when it's time to come in
I tap on the bin.
When it's time for dinner,
I am always a winner.
He sleeps on the chair
Which gets covered in hair,
Then he plays with string
That gets chucked in the bin.

Leah Jones (10)
Bigyn CP School

LOVE

Love is really important to me,
Love is something you sometimes see.
Love is something you have to show,
Love is something you're sure to know.
When you and someone are in love,
As people say, you might feel like a dove.
If someone tells you you've got a heart full of gold,
It might be love, so I've been told.

Jade Campion (10)
Bigyn CP School

HOOK'S TREASURE

In 1563 the pirates sailed the seas,
Searching for the treasure, it gave them so much pleasure.
The leader's name was Hook, he had a nasty look.
No one he would thank, he just made them walk the plank.

Other pirates he would cross, he'd soon show them who was boss.
Hook quickly buried all the gold, and no one he ever told.
He wrote the clues down on a map, but then set up some nasty traps.
No one has ever found his lair and if they go hunting, they'd
better beware!

Maddison Shakes (9)
Bigyn CP School

BARNEY

Barney is my dog,
He's been known to get lost in the fog.
He's scared of the water and rain,
In the winter, walking him is a real pain.
When the doorbell rings,
He starts to sing,
But his best songs are sung in the morning,
When I'm still yawning.

Jack Hart (9)
Bigyn CP School

MY WEEKEND

I like my weekends away,
When I can go out to play.
I go to my grandparents' caravan
And sometimes I even catch a tan.

There are many things to do,
Like swimming, riding, a visit to the zoo.
When night falls, it's off to the pub
To play bingo and have some grub.

So soon the weekend is over
And we return home in our Rover.
Then we get ready for the week ahead,
Then it's off to bed, you sleepyhead.

Leanne Morgan (9)
Bigyn CP School

WINTER

W hite, fluffy snow,
I cy roads and frozen feet,
N uts to eat and crackers to pull,
T insel and Christmas trees.
E venings draw in and days are cold,
R ed robins chirping in the trees.

Nicolle Gimblett (7)
Bigyn CP School

MY DOG HOLLY

My dog Holly is a very jolly dog,
My dog Holly is a very clever dog,
My dog Holly can do silly tricks,
My dog Holly likes to fetch sticks,
My dog Holly is only six.
I love my dog Holly, I love her to bits.

Damian Williams (8)
Bigyn CP School

THE LOST TREASURE

On the sandy beach
Lies the buried treasure.
If you want to find it,
You will have to measure.

Ten feet north and
Six feet west,
Dig on that spot,
Then take a rest.

Dig some more
Till you find the gold,
The story of the missing treasure
Has been told.

Rebecca Bradbeer (10)
Bigyn CP School

HIDDEN TREASURE

Hidden treasure,
So I'm told,
Consists of gems
And yellow gold.

To find the treasure
I have a map,
But first of all
I must find a tap.

The tap I find
Next to a rock,
It also had
A very big lock.

I search the sand
For a key,
Just me and my map,
Next to the sea.

I find the key
Inside a cave
And jump with joy
And give a wave.

I run to the tap
And grab the lock
And insert the key
Next to the rock.

Beneath the sand
A big brown chest,
Ten steps north
And five steps west.

I opened the chest
With eyes open wide,
My mouth gaping open,
I never noticed the tide.

I quickly grabbed
What treasure I found
And swiftly ran on
Without a sound.

My treasure, I discovered,
Was not gems and gold,
But a secret,
Never to be told.

Jamie Rogers (9)
Bigyn CP School

CAPTAIN JACK AND THE STORM

You can call me Captain Jack,
The pirate of the seas.
A shark took my leg off one day,
Now I've got a wooden peg up to my knee.

I fell overboard into the sea
One wild and stormy day,
The clouds were nearly black as night,
The wind so strong I was blown away.

That is where I met the shark,
Under the high, choppy waves.
It was just luck he let me go,
And thank God, I was saved.

The boat was nearly tipped upside down,
The wind tore right through the sails.
We started in Timbuktu
And the wind blew us to Wales.

Nathan Moorhouse (9)
Bigyn CP School

THE FISH

There was a fish
That made a wish
That if he took the bait,
He wouldn't end up on my plate.

His name was Spot,
He really knew a lot.
His best friend Elly,
Who was rather smelly.

They live in a tank,
With their best friend, Frank,
Who swam around
Without making a sound.

Craig Williams (10)
Bigyn CP School

BURIED TREASURE

On the beach the sand was hot,
The waves trickled by.
I saw some palm trees, tall and green,
Then something caught my eye.

A shining colour of green and red
Was picked up by the sun.
I walked along to this shimmering light,
But then I had to run.

Before me was a wooden chest,
My eyes had seen no pleasure.
I opened the lid, my face lit up
As I gazed at the buried treasure.

Liam Jones (9)
Bigyn CP School

SHOP 'TIL YOU DROP

I like to shop on the weekends,
With a bunch of my best friends.

We go to many different shops
To try on many types of tops.

Tammy, New Look, you know what,
You can find us at the lot.

Woolworths we go for some sweets,
Oh how yummy, what a treat.

Then we need a little break,
So we buy a large milkshake.

Then we're ready to shop again,
Stationery Box for a pen.

Bargains are what we try to find,
So our mothers won't really mind.

Then we're done for the day,
Wishing that we could stay.

My rule is that I don't stop,
I shop, shop, shop until I drop!

Natalie Jones (11)
Bigyn CP School

MY TEDDY

My teddy bear gets up at night
And dances all night long,
Then he gets an awful fright
When he does something wrong.

When he hears a little sound,
He hides under the chair,
Then he looks around
To see if anyone's there.

When he is bored, he goes downstairs,
Holding onto the wall.
He sits on one of five chairs
To watch some football.

When he sees the morning light,
He goes back to bed,
Because he knows it is not night,
But to rest his nice head.

Sarah Caul (10)
Bigyn CP School

MY FAVOURITE BOOK

Harry Potter is an eleven-year-old boy,
His enemy is Draco Malfoy.
Harry is unhappy, but very gifted,
When he goes to Hogwarts, his spirits are lifted.
Ron Weasley and Hermione Granger,
His friends' names couldn't be much stranger,
And when Harry gets into trouble,
They're there to pull him out of the rubble.
In the aerial game, Quidditch, Harry plays Seeker.
His catching abilities couldn't be sleeker.
To win the game, he catches the Snitch,
Bringing it down safely onto the pitch.

I think the books are really cool,
I ready them every night after school,
Before I go swimming in the pool.
As soon as I return, I sit back down,
Pick up a book to remove my tired frown.
Clever J K Rowling, deserves a crown,
With her imagination, she's out on her own.

Steven Pettiford (11)
Bigyn CP School

The Little Stream

Through drapes of tangled hanging weed,
Through all the oak trees' boughs,
Lying in the open breeze,
The little stream flows now.

It used to be a beautiful lake,
But the winter days came near.
The only thing that was left of it
Was a hole in the rock pool here!

Little drips drop through the hole,
Forming the new-found stream.
Everything looks better now,
For it's small and growing dreams!

Lucy Aubrey (10)
Bigyn CP School

TREASURE

There lies a trunk of treasure,
If you find it there'll be pleasure.
Rich, rich, you'll be,
No more fighting, you'll see.
More treasure for me.
Open the lid, you'll be rich,
You could buy a rugby pitch.

Kristian Evans (10)
Bigyn CP School

I Am A Treasure Chest

I am a treasure chest,
Buried deep underground.
Please someone find me,
I'm dying to be found.

I am a treasure chest,
I can make you rich,
I'm hidden on an island
Beneath a crumbling ditch.

I am a treasure chest,
I'll never make you frown,
I've got diamonds and shiny pearls
And even a golden crown.

Kieran Davies (11)
Bigyn CP School

THE LOST TREASURE

When I went to the beach,
There was something sticking out of the sand.
I picked it up,
It was quite old, it was a map!
I read it, it was leading to the cave.
I went to the cave, but there was nothing there.
It must need a password.
I guessed a few words, but nothing happened.
Then, where I was standing, the floor *shook!*
Then the caved opened and
There stood the treasure that had been lost for centuries.

Chelsea Rees (10)
Bigyn CP School

STARS

Stars are so bright,
They shine in the night
And twinkle like fairies,
Like pretty red berries.
They lie so high in the sky,
Oh, how I wish I could fly.

Taleah Richards (8)
Bigyn CP School

COLOURS

Yellow for wheat,
Yellow for the sun,
Yellow for a sweet,
And yellow for a bun.

Red for a rose,
Red for a top,
Red for a nose
And red for pop.

Blue for the sky,
Blue for a pen,
Blue for your eye
And blue for men.

Amy Stanlake (9)
Bigyn CP School

STARS

Stars that smile,
Stars that shine,
In a line,
Side by side.

Stars that are loving,
Stars that are sad,
Stars that are caring
And stars that are bad.

Stars that are lonely,
Shining on me,
Stars that are lovely,
That I can see.

Sadie George (8)
Bigyn CP School

MY SCHOOL

My school is so cool,
The school dinners make me drool.
Yellow custard, thick and creamy,
Makes my glasses go all steamy.

There is lots of work for everyone
And after work, we have some fun.
I play netball in the yard,
Because the rugby is too hard.

Back to class after play,
For the last lesson of the day.
We pack our bags ready to go
And when the bell goes, we walk out the door.

Rachel Merriman (9)
Bigyn CP School

THE FROZEN AIR

The frozen air was all glittering,
Gazing,
Sparkling,
Whizzing,
Crazing,
Lazing,
Shining,
It was amazing,
It was like crystal,
And that was what the frozen air looked like.

Naomi Smith (8)
Bigyn CP School

BEACH

One day I was on the beach,
The water was very calm,
Sand was like golden treasure,
There were fish jumping out of the sea
While I was drinking my tea,
My brother had his Coke,
While Father did his backstroke.

Shaun Hopkins (9)
Bigyn CP School

ABOUT SCHOOL

S chool is the best,
C ome and see us work,
H ere we do English and then we do maths,
O utside we play, having fun with our friends,
O h no, in we have to go.
L ots more to do before the bell rings to go home.

Hope Harries (9)
Bigyn CP School

FAR STAR

I looked above and saw a star
And I said, 'It is very far.'
I said, 'It is very light
And I bet it shines all night.'

Is my star there in the day,
Watching me talk and play?
I hope my star is out tonight
For me to say goodnight.

I named my star Kay
And it will not be there in May.
I looked above and saw a star,
And said, 'It is very far.'

Nadia Suliman (9)
Bigyn CP School

BEACH

One day I went to the beach
And I tanned and tanned until I was peach.
The sun was shining and
The sea was sparkling,
The sun was so bright it hurt my eyes.
I went in the sea with my friends.
All day long we went in and out,
We'd never stop the fun
So we carried on playing until we had to go.

Bianca Morris (8)
Bigyn CP School

MY NOISY GRANDPA

My grandpa didn't sleep last night,
Well, that's what he told me.
But I heard such and awful noise
That I went to see.

I peeped my head around his door,
The noise that he was making,
I shouted out for help to come,
I thought the bed was breaking.

My mum and dad came charging in,
'Where's the fire?' they said.
But my grandpa he just lay there,
Snoring in his bed.

So, the next time grandpa tells me
'I didn't sleep last night!'
I think I'll have to tell him,
Yeah, right!

Kassie Foden (11)
Felinfoel Junior School

MY CAT MAGGIE

I have a cat called Maggie,
That's a black and ginger tabby.
She's strong and very long,
She sleeps on a mat
And is getting very fat.
She's not at all mean,
But she likes herself clean,
And that's my cat, Maggie.

Aaron Williams
Felinfoel Junior School

WHO RULES OUR HOUSE?

Dad's the boss,
Or so he thinks,
But when he turns,
My mammy winks.

He says, 'I rule.'
He thinks he's cool,
But we all know
When we're in school,
Mammy has the golden rule.

Mammy's the boss,
Dad's at a loss
For words when Mammy gets cross.
We all stand
And obey the command.

Rhys Harries (11)
Felinfoel Junior School

MY BROTHER

This poem is about my brother,
Who is definitely not like any other.
He eats and talks a lot,
And his favourite dog is Spot.

Tweenies is his favourite programme on telly,
And he's quiet when he's filling his belly.
He jumps and screams all day long,
And when he fills his nappy, he doesn't half pong!

At eight o'clock he goes to bed,
As my mother tells him he's going on his head.
He snuggles up nice and warm,
Better get ready, he gets up at dawn.

Jade Howells (10)
Felinfoel Junior School

THE ZIT ON MY FACE

Monday morning when I woke up
I nearly had a fit.
I screamed and screamed,
Because I had a horrible *zit!*

It was big, it was huge,
It was enormous, it was terrifying,
But my family thought
It was petrifying.

It seemed to
Grow and grow
But what I truly hated
Was that it seemed to glow.

Poor zit!
My mum has
Just squeezed it.
After all, it wasn't that bad.

Elinor Morris (9)
Felinfoel Junior School

MY GROOVY OLD GRAN

My groovy old gran
Is one of a kind,
She's way past eighty
And out of her mind.

She's been everywhere
And done everything,
She loves a good dance
And loves a good sing.

She's travelled to Kenya,
China and Chile,
She brought back a snake.
I think she's plain silly.

She goes scuba-diving,
Kayaking as well.
She also goes skiing
And does them all well.

She loves down the disco
Every Saturday night,
With all her great moves,
She's an eye-popping sight.

Although she is crazy
And acts like the fool,
At the end of the day,
I still think she's cool.

Gemma Gibbs (10)
Felinfoel Junior School

GONE FISHING

I place a worm upon a hook
To catch a fish that I can cook.

I cast my line into the deep
And watch the fish as they leap.

I know I will catch a fish,
So I can eat it from my dish.

I catch a fish in my net,
The rain comes down and I get wet.

In the sky I see a cloud form,
I must get home before the storm.

Eve Evans (10)
Felinfoel Junior School

FALLING ASLEEP

Voices from the rooms,
My cat breathing heavily at the end of my bed,
I can smell the Olbas oil on my pillow.
I can hear my brother playing the PlayStation.
I begin to dream . . .

Natalie Rees (10)
Felinfoel Junior School

WHAT AM I?

I am as white as a sheet
And have got lots of black spots.
I love to eat meat.
Sometimes I run and hide.

I hate to be nagged,
I also live in a house,
I hate to be combed,
I have long white teeth.

I have my little red toy,
I love to drink milk,
I am a male.
What am I?

Rebecca Davies (11)
Felinfoel Junior School

ANIMALS

The golden lion sleeps for twenty hours a day,
Takes four hours to seek prey.

The monkey is grey and
Easy to see from far away.

The spider eats and eats
But gets no wider.

The blue tit is a little too small,
Eating worms and sitting on the wall.

The big brown bear likes to roar,
Breaks down the door.

The red kite is so rare to see,
You won't find many perched in a tree.

The mouse steals the cheese
From the cupboard, what a little creep.

The ants carry leaves,
Which they like to hide away, so nobody sees.

Ashley Thomas (9)
Ffairfach Primary School

TREASURE OF THE DEEP

A sunken ship
At the bottom of the sea.
Who will find
The treasures for you and me?

A sunken ship
With secrets for us to see,
So very, very deep,
It may be best to leave it be.

David Ralph (11)
Ffairfach Primary School

DOWN BENEATH THE OCEAN BLUE

Down beneath the ocean blue,
What you want to see may be very rare.
You may see an octopus or just a fish,
Nobody knows.

How about treasure guarded by sharks?
Maybe some jellyfish covered with pearls,
Swimming around gaily?
Nobody knows.

I wish I could see them all, but
I know I see them in my dreams.

Caryl Williams (9)
Ffairfach Primary School

NEW YORK CITY

New York City is so big
And so tall,

There is no wildlife,
None at all.

New York City is so crowded,
Full of cars,

I wish aliens could
Take it up to Mars.

Down in Vermont the sun
Is shining bright,

Up in California, the
Thunder is a fright.

The skyscrapers are
So high in the sky,

It's hard for birds
To try and fly.

Ffion Evans (10)
Ffairfach Primary School

SUPER RAT

You could say
He's a pest.
You could say
He's vermin.

He couldn't
Fly higher
Than a tree

But he saves
All those rats
From those
Nasty old cats.

He tried to
Save a rat,
But got caught,
And that was that.

Joshua Burns (9)
Ffairfach Primary School

SWIMMING IN THE SEA

Swim in the ocean, swim in the sea,
Mumbles beach is the place to be.
Swim in the ocean, swim in the sea,
Jumping up and down, just like me.
Here comes a jellyfish, here is a crab,
This is so brilliant, this is so fab.

Rebecca Dawson (9)
Ffairfach Primary School

THE SUN

There's never been a long straight lane
Without a single bend.
There never was an uphill road
That did not have an end.
It's quite unknown for a cloudy sky
Which has not turned to blue,
For always if you watch and wait
The sun comes shining through.

Joshua Thomas (10)
Ffairfach Primary School

THE BONFIRE

The evil bonfire is burning your eyes,
It is like the red-hot steam of a volcano.
He is ready for danger.
A sparkling bonfire of jewels.
The bonfire has eaten away the grass,
Now the guy is going to melt.
It was a *gigantic* bonfire,
But now it is dead.
Now all I can see are ashes on the ground.

Lucy Gough (9)
Ffairfach Primary School

FLAMENCO DANCERS

Flamenco dancers, who are they?
Dancing on the floor,
Wearing white silk dresses
With lace and frills galore.

In their hands are castanets
With pictures painted on.
Sometimes they have a partner,
At times they dance alone.

They always dance to Spanish sounds,
The flamenco's my favourite dance.
People clapping all at once,
It's like they're in a trance!

The party goes on all through the night
And never stops to rest.
People there are very nice,
I think they are the best.

So there you are, my rhyme is done,
As I hear that happy sound
Of flamenco dancers' busy feet
Tapping on the ground.

Harriet Gibson (11)
Ffairfach Primary School

THE DEEP BLUE SEA

The deep blue sea is a dangerous place,
Boats and gold disappear without a trace.
Monsters in the sea like sharks, eels and rays,
Wander in the water as if it was a maze.

But at night, the sea is calm,
It moves back and forth like a pendulum.
There are many things we need to see,
But the most spectacular has to be the sea.

Huw Llewelyn (11)
Ffairfach Primary School

THE SEA

In the sea, there are lots of things you can see.
The sea is the place I want to be.
Electric eels and sharks are all my favourite fish,
But the best one has to be the jellyfish.

Jon Llewelyn (9)
Ffairfach Primary School

IF I COULD BE AN ANIMAL

If I could be an animal,
I would be
A lion,
Wild and free.

If I could be an animal,
I would be
An elephant,
Taller than any tree.

If I could be an animal,
I would be
A giraffe,
Everything to see.

If I could be an animal,
I would be
A dolphin,
Swimming over the ocean sea.

But for now,
I think I'll stay
Me,
Just for a day.

Bethan Hughes (11)
Ffairfach Primary School

WELSH SCENERY

Have you seen gloomy Wales
Full of slaughtered sheep and cows?
What about the sunken pits,
Full of water, stones and grit?

Have you seen beautiful Wales,
The lovely scenery of mountains?
How about the forestry,
And all the pretty fountains?

Philip Thomas (11)
Llanybydder Primary School

HAIKU

Are you coming out?
We can go and call for Jo.
OK let's go then.

Shall we go shopping?
Yes, but will your mum let you?
Let's go and ask her.

Shall I buy this top?
How much is it? Fourteen pounds
I'll go and pay then.

Shall we go to Spar?
Why? What are you going to buy?
Some crisps and more sweets.

Let's go to school now.
Are you going to drama?
I will ask my mum.

Kristina Davies (11)
Llanybydder Primary School

THE SEA

The sea is whistling quietly,
But the fish are swimming along,
The crabs are sleeping and snoring.

The dolphins and whales are doing tricks,
The starfish clap delightfully
And so do the fish.

It's not a noisy day down in the sea,
Everybody is tired from clapping
And doing tricks.

Hedydd Wilson (10)
Llanybydder Primary School

PIRATES AND TREASURES

Hidden treasure is a wonderful thing,
Pirates dig for it as they sing,
Although the ship of 'Scumbag Bet'
Haven't found their treasure yet.

They've searched on land, day and night,
They've fought in wars and terrible fights.
The captain's men have died a terrible death,
By fighting a dragon and being blown by his breath.

The captain always says, 'We'll find it,'
But we haven't found a little bit.
But then one night, a fearful night,
The lookout shouted, 'There's land in sight.'

They rowed and rowed in the seas of sour,
They were going faster and faster in the miles per hour.
Suddenly, they stopped, they'd hit land
And they were helped down by the captain's hand.

The captain fell over, what a funny sight,
They didn't know what would happen, it would most probably
                                        be a fight.
The captain very slowly got up (with a bump on his head),
Then he said, 'You nearly got me dead!'

They started to dig, dig and dig,
The hole got big, as big as a crib.
Then they hit a bit of wood
And it wasn't wood, it was a hood.

They pulled it out and opened it up,
They thought it was the treasure with any luck,
But no, it was a ball and the captain swore in Latin.
'Better luck next time, then,' said the captain.

Daniel Farmer (11)
Llanybydder Primary School

RUGBY

The whistle blows
And the ball is in the air,
The forwards jump
Then comes a clunk
And the ref has had a bump.

There goes a try
And now it's even,
The players putting away,
The outside half has missed
The easy conversion,
But how could that be?
Wales are in the lead.

The score is tied now,
Twenty all and it's very close,
But what is this?
Jenkins has had a penalty,
Yes, it's over,
And now we have won!

Rhydian Davies (10)
Llanybydder Primary School

WALES

Have you been to Wales?
If you have not,
You will never see the true glamour
Of the scenery, farms,
And all of our lambs and sheep.
At least have a peep
So you can see the true glamour
Of our small country.

Wales, Wales, my beautiful country,
You go there and see the beauty,
But if you fly over and over,
You see its true beauty.
Farms, sheep, cattle, houses, sheds, barns,
Only then you see its true beauty.
Wales, Wales, fly over Wales.

Huw Chandler (11)
Llanybydder Primary School

WALES TODAY

In Wales today, on the hill,
There are trees and animals.
When I go to school, we play,
Enjoy ourselves and we do work.

Every year we have a market,
We buy stuff and
We have holidays from school.

Wales is the place to be,
So don't go, please stay and
Have fun here with me.

Sonia Mills (10)
Llanybydder Primary School

WALES

Wales has a rugby team,
When people watch, they all scream.
When they score a try,
On the floor they sit or lie.

In Wales, there are lots of mountains
And lots of people have fountains.
In the trees they have lots of lines,
In the olden days, there were a lot of mines.

In Wales we have lots of schools,
Lots of people have tools,
Lots like playing football
And lots get hurt with a fall.

Shaun Jacob (11)
Llanybydder Primary School

FLOWERS

Flowers are so soft,
Sweet and bright,
Only when the sun comes out.
They smell sweet and fresh,
The night comes out,
The sun goes down,
The flowers go to sleep.

Troy Mealing (8)
Llangunnor Primary School

SWIMMING LESSONS

I'm having swimming lessons at the local pool,
I'm hoping one day soon I will look super cool.
My teacher is Marie, she's teaching me to swim,
She says I need to eat more, because I am quite thin.
A little bit of fat would help me to float,
But me, I just sink like the Titanic boat.

Elliot Lewis (8)
Llangunnor Primary School

WHERE DO THEY ALL COME FROM?

There you are on the floor,
There are more behind the door.

There must be loads under my bed,
Where have the rest of you all fled?

Cotton and wool, all different sorts,
I even have short ones, just for sports.

The old, the new, the red and the blue,
I just can't find them, not a clue!

I really need to get some locks
To stop me finding all these odd socks!

Sophie Jenkins (8)
Llangunnor Primary School

TEENAGERS

Teenagers as spotty as leopards,
Ugly as pigs,
So bossy and selfish,
Fat and chubby,
Just stupid and lazy like hippos,
Very hairy, like bears,
Never eat at school
But always eat at home,
Never do their work,
Just watch TV or play the computer,
Rather get wet than wear a coat,
Never think of other people,
And they always play the fool,
Thinking they are cool.

Philip Adams (9)
Llangunnor Primary School

MY PARENTS

I love you Mum,
I love you Dad,
I love you both
And I am glad.

I love you
With all my heart,
That's why I care for you,
My mum and dad.

You buy me toys
With a lot of care,
You take me places,
Everywhere.

You love my brother with all your care,
And that is why
He goes anywhere,
And so do I.

You try to please me
And my brother too.
You make us happy
Through and through.

Joel Wray (8)
Llangunnor Primary School

UNDERWATER

I have always wanted to see what it is like to swim underwater,
Where the proud fishes lurk through the coral
Standing smartly on the floor of the seabed.
Jellyfish and octopus glooming through the dark ocean sea,
Squid trying to avoid treacherous predators swimming through
The damp and leafy seaweed, ready to catch prey and have lunch.
The sharks will be hungry no longer.
Two whales are mating, ready to have children in their lives,
In a quiet lagoon, peaceful enough for anything not to disturb.
And my favourite of them all, the starfishes twirling and swirling,
Gliding and sliding and spinning with glee on the bright ocean surface.

Rhys Schelewa-Davies (8)
Llangunnor Primary School

TWO DIFFERENT DAYS

One sunny day,
The sun is shining up above.
It's getting really hot,
The sky is blue,
There's plenty to do
On a hot, sunny day.

One miserable day
In the wind and the rain,
The storm clouds are gathering,
The rain falls,
There's nothing to do
In the wind and the rain.

Laura Penhallurick (8)
Llangunnor Primary School

THINGS ABOUT MONSTERS

Monsters are brown,
Monsters are black
And one always says,
'Get off my back.'

Monsters are red,
Monsters are green,
I don't care about their colours,
I don't like them when they're mean.

David Bowen (9)
Llangunnor Primary School

PENGUIN POEM

Penguins, penguins, cold and wet,
Penguins, penguins, can't keep them as a pet.
Penguins, penguins, swimming in the ocean,
Penguins, penguins, can't make a potion.

Penguins, penguins, slipping on ice,
Penguins, penguins, slipping over twice.
Penguins, penguins, white, yellow and black,
Penguins, penguins, staying in a pack.

Penguins, penguins, they are cute,
Penguins, penguins are never mute.
Penguins, penguins, eating fish,
Penguins, penguins, never on a dish.

Ceri Ann Benjamin (9)
Llangunnor Primary School

ALL ALONE

Out on the street I am all alone
In this darkening world of mine.
The shine of the sun is all I have,
The rags I wear are so cold and bare,
I'm all alone in the world.
The stream running through the trees,
I sleep on a bed of autumn leaves.
I eat fruit and berries
And at Christmas I don't make merry.
Fine people turn their noses up at the sight of me,
Others just leave me be,
But the one thing I have in this world
Is the shine of the sun, inside me.

Sophie Hill (9)
Llangunnor Primary School

THE FLOOD

It rained all day,
It rained all night,
The wind it blew
The birds from sight.

Up came the river,
It got deeper and deeper,
The pavements and roads
Did not need a road sweeper.

Until the end,
The rain did stop
And left a large tree.
On the roads, start to mop.

Terri Ann Davies (8)
Llangunnor Primary School

TO MY MAM

I love you,
You're like a circle in my heart.
You're mine,
We'll never be apart.

Jack Evans (9)
Llangunnor Primary School

CATS

Cats are lovely,
Nice and furry,
They like you when you're nice to them,
And they'll love you every day,
And they like to play.

Stephanie Morris (8)
Llangunnor Primary School

AT THE SEASIDE

At the seaside
There is a stall
Which always sells ice creams
And lots of balls.

At the seaside
The sea is getting near,
A nice light blue,
It is very clear.

At the seaside,
The sun has gone down,
It's time to pack up
And go back to town.

Katie Arnold (8)
Llangunnor Primary School

GIRLS RULE

Girls rule, girls are cool,
They like to go shopping
And go clip-clopping
In high-heeled shoes.
Girls rule!

Hebe Young (8)
Llangunnor Primary School

MY RABBIT

My rabbit's name is Floppy,
He is as white as snow,
He eats all day
And sleeps all night,
That is what rabbits do,
So that is alright.

Tara Williams (8)
Llangunnor Primary School

TREASURES UNDER THE SEA

T   reasure, treasure under the sea,
R   ugged stones beside the quay,
E   very fish guards it carefully,
A   s you open it and look amazingly,
S   hining bright is a gold ring,
U   ncertain as to its destiny
R   olling around fit for a king,
E   nduring the waves masterfully.

Stuart Havard (8)
Llangunnor Primary School

THE TIGER

The tiger is a beautiful creature,
He lives in a dark, gloomy, creepy, damp jungle,
He's a sly and silent beast.
He pounces at his prey,
The tiger is a sly slayer and a killer.
The cat camouflages himself in the long deep grass,
The beast is a fierce devious animal,
With a deafening roar,
As he devours his prey
With dagger-sharp teeth.

Natasha Frazer (11)
Ponthenri Primary School

THE TIGER

Prowling through the darkness,
Searching for his prey,
Killing the victim with his dagger-sharp teeth,
The tiger camouflages himself before he attacks.
Roaming through the jungle,
Defending his young,
Roaring his deafening roar,
The cat has great courage,
Protecting his mate,
The graceful slayer.

Garin Griffiths (9)
Ponthenri Primary School

FEAR

A shiver ran down my spine
When Mum said that vampire doll was mine.
Fear when Emma turned green in my class,
Fear of long snakes camouflaged in the grass.
Fear of dentists drilling into my teeth,
Fear of dark shadows on a tiny leaf.
Fear of dogs with sharp, dagger teeth,
Fear of rats. Argh! Good grief.
Fear of wind blowing the curtains at night,
Fear of walking in the graveyard without light.
Fear of shadows in the woods,
Fear of getting caught in the rain without a hood.
Fear of spiders with long hairy legs in the bath, so deep,
Fear of giants taking a big, enormous leap.
Fear of Hallowe'en when people come trick or treating,
Fear of black cats in the night. Argh! Is that a rat it's eating?

Melissa Bennett (11)
Ponthenri Primary School

FEAR

A shiver ran down my spine,
As a mean vampire thought I was divine.
When Dad fell down the sink,
When Mum went mad and dyed her hair pink!
When I'm home alone at night
The witches give me a fright.
It scared me out of my wits,
When the whole world had nits.
When I opened the door to Dracula,
He fought me and laughed, ha, ha, ha.
My horrid fears of the night
They give me a dreadful fright.

Emily Fletcher-Miles (11)
Ponthenri Primary School

THE LION

The lion home is at the jungle,
Camouflaged in the tall green grass,
He kills animals with is dagger-sharp teeth.
Lions roar very loud,
Their paws are razor-sharp.
In the deadly night he hunts for food.
His home is dark and eerie,
He walks slowly and silently in the dark mysterious jungle.
The lion is king.

Luke Bennett (9)
Ponthenri Primary School

THE LION

The lion is a killer,
So fierce and sly,
Lives in the jungle,
Gloomy and dark,
Razor-sharp teeth
And deadly claws,
Beautiful fur,
Camouflaged in grass,
Carnivorous beast,
Ready to slaughter,
Blood! Blood! Blood!

Wayne Jones (10)
Ponthenri Primary School

FEAR!

A shiver ran down my spine
In a dark graveyard at night,
There were noises that gave me a fright.
Dogs barking, with dagger-sharp teeth,
And the wind howling through every leaf.
Thunder and lightning going *crash, bang, cleck!*
And water coming over top deck.
I found a big hairy spider in the bath,
It scares me when Miss tells me to do maths.
Walking home in the night,
It gives me an awful fright.
Thirteen fears at night,
They always give me a horrid fright.

Sarah Jones (11)
Ponthenri Primary School

THE LION

The lion roars loudly,
He sits on Pride Rock proudly,
He devours his prey with his dagger-sharp teeth
And when he consumes his dinner there is no relief.
A lion is vicious,
His food, he thinks is delicious.
He has sensitive hearing,
When he is happy, he is purring.
On his prey he does pounce
And he doesn't leave an ounce,
A lion is a beast,
Every day he does feast.

Maddie Hinkin (9)
Ponthenri Primary School

THE LION

The king of the jungle,
With dagger-sharp teeth and deadly claws,
Roams slowly through the long green grass
Searching for his innocent prey.
He sees his victim on the horizon,
He knows full well it's not his poison.
Slowly he creeps among the plains,
Attacking the buffalo gives him great pain,
The buffalo makes a deafening noise
As his life comes to an end.
Along come the cubs for their lunch
While the mother keeps vultures away from her playful bunch.

Sara Griffiths (11)
Ponthenri Primary School

LOOKING THROUGH THE WINDOW

As I stare through the window,
I see the milkman rushing,
The newspaper boy dashing,
All to avoid a drenching.

As I watch the water trickling
Down the misty window,
The rain is pouring
And the children are splashing.

As I look out of the window,
I see the birds in the trees hiding,
While the cars whizz past
With wipers working fast.

As I stare out of the window,
I know the wind is blowing
To make the trees waver
And the leaves quiver.

As I look out of the window
At last the sun is shining
And over there in the sky,
A multicoloured rainbow glistening high.

Nia Beynon (10)
Saron CP School

WHEN I GROW UP

When I grow up, I'd like to see the stars,
Mercury, Venus alongside Mars.
I'd watch the stars from my bedroom,
Through a telescope with a nice big zoom.

When I grow up I'd like to be a cook,
I'd learn it from a cookery book,
Not from a packet, or not from a tin,
I'd invite my friends for a nice night in.

When I grow up I'd like to be on the news,
Interviewing and doing reviews.
Watch me on GMTV and ITN,
Or stay up late and I'll be on the News at Ten.

When I grow up, I don't know what I'll be.
One thing's for sure, I'll still be me!

Thomas Giffard (10)
Saron CP School

I LOVE BOOKS

I like to read best at home,
When it's quiet and I'm on my own.
Best of all I like the night,
In my bed, wrapped up tight.

This is my time I like to look
At pages and words, it's called a book.
Tales of places I've never been,
Exciting stories to keep me keen.

Dahl, Wilson, Rowling and Stein,
I like to read twice every line.
Animals, people, adventures and spooks,
I find all these in my books.

Rhiannon Sheen de Jesus (9)
Saron CP School

Dogs

Dogs are great,
They're absolutely fun,
They're full of energy,
Exercising as much as they can.

They do many exciting things,
And they're really cool.
They love chasing cats,
Acting like complete fools.

They're really amazing,
Running through grass,
Strange looks on their faces
As they let people pass.

Dogs are cute,
They're the best.
They love their owners
'Cause they're better than the rest.

Charlotte Jones (10)
Saron CP School

RAIN

I like the rain.
Most people don't,
But I do.
I like to run around
And get wet,
Through and through.

I don't like it when
I have to sit inside,
I want to go out
And run about,
Because I enjoy
To scream and shout.

Nia Dowley (11)
Saron CP School

MY PETS

First there's my fish,
Who for some are the top dish.
They could probably swim a mile
And get eaten by a crocodile.
Some of them can be pretty,
Although they're slimy and squiggly.

My guinea pigs and rabbit
Have very bad habits,
They eat each others poo
And they like to go to the loo
In the corner of the cage
And my mother stamps in rage.

And finally, there's my cat
Who marks her territory on the mat.
She pukes up on the chair
And we never know it's there.
She's better than the other six,
Even though she knows no tricks.

My mother wants to get rid of my pets,
She says that she really needs a rest.
But I don't want to get rid of them
Because they are the best.

Robin Ramsurrun (10)
Saron CP School

THE PICNIC

One sunny morning,
I woke up stretching and yawning,
Wondering what we would do today
On the second day of May.

So up I got
Like a shot to see my mum and dad.
I walked up to their room and had a peep,
But they were both still fast asleep.

So up they got from their slumber
And we all helped do the sandwiches with cucumber.
So we all got in the car to Pembrey Park,
To have a picnic and a lark.

We brought a ball, bucket and spade,
So we put up our umbrella to get some shade,
Then we sat down on the sand,
Then my dad asked for a hand.

Many sandcastles that day were made,
Whilst my mother just laid in the shade,
Bodyboards in hand as we walked on the sand,
To have some fun in the waves.

We splished and we splashed and had good fun,
We were having a wonderful time in the sun.
After some hours, it was time to go back,
As the sky was becoming very black.

Geraint Newton-Walker (10)
Saron CP School

SCHOOL IS GREAT!

School is lovely,
School is great,
But school is best
Outside the gate.

Sums and writing
Are all right,
No! to homework
Every night.

I don't mind writing,
I like to read,
What I like best
Is quarter-past three.

Welsh is the best,
English is all right,
Maths is cool,
Sometimes science gives me a fright.

But after all the working,
The thing that I like best
Is football during play time,
It gives us all a rest.

Dafydd Thomas (9)
Saron CP School

THE PYRAMID

I was in the desert,
It was very warm,
I saw a pyramid
Then there was a sandstorm.

I saw a big stone
Which looked like a door,
I pushed it open,
Would inside be a bore?

I felt the ground sinking,
Then shouted, 'Oh no!'
I saw strange markings
As I fell through a trapdoor.

I stood up and looked around,
There was lots of gold.
I could not believe my eyes,
By now I was very cold.

I saw a statue,
Then a big gold cup,
Something cold touched my cheek,
'Rhydian, it is time to get up.'

Rhydian Cooper (9)
Saron CP School

MY FAMILY ARE WEIRD

My mum is a monster,
My dad is a boxer
And my brother can't get more hideous
Than Shrek, who's an ogre.

My uncle is rich,
My granny is poor
And we were in-between,
But not any more!

So this is the last verse
That I have written,
And I'd better finish it quick,
Before I get bitten!

Robert Hearne (9)
Saron CP School

FOOD

From wheat we make bread
And wash it down with wine,
As long as it does not go to my head,
The feeling of fullness is mine.

Bananas come from a hot country
And very good they are,
But if the skins fall to the floor,
Slip on them we will, ha, ha!

Potatoes are a basic vegetable,
You use them for chips as well,
But if we eat too many of them,
We'll look like a bell.

Apples and pears we grow at home,
They last all winter long,
But if we drop them on the ground,
They bruise and then they are gone.

When Mammy does a lot of cooking,
We all have lots to eat,
But if we eat it all,
The dog won't have any treats.

Strawberries and raspberries grow in the summer,
We love to go and pick them,
But if we eat too many,
We have a bad belly.

Brown bread is really healthy,
But white is what we like,
So if I eat a lot of it,
I'll have the energy to ride my bike.

Oranges are my favourite fruit,
I eat them all the time,
But when my mammy has not bought them,
I think it's a crime.

Laura Powell (10)
Saron CP School

SEASONS

Winter is cold and dark
And I can't go to play in the park.
Days are short and nights so long,
There're not many birds to sing a song.

When the plants and leaves begin to grow
And the snowdrops start to show,
This is when I like to sing
Because it is the start of spring.

Then the cold goes and out comes the sun
And I know I can have some fun.
Summer's arrived, I go on holiday
And when I'm home, I can go out and play.

When the leaves go brown and fall
And the sun forgets to call,
I know that means autumn's here
And soon we'll begin another year.

Catherine Pritchard (10)
Saron CP School

FOOTBALL

Football is my favourite game,
Every Saturday it is the same,
We play a match, home or away,
It really is my favourite day.

Every Wednesday we go training,
When we get there it is always raining.
My job is to try and score,
One, two, three or more.

We have a good team from front to back,
Defenders, midfield and a fantastic attack.
When I play football, I have such fun,
Especially after a game that we have won.

Oliver Ardolino (10)
Saron CP School

MY DOG KYRA

My dog Kyra is so sweet,
She likes eating cooked meat.
She likes running around,
Always staying on the ground.

My dog Kyra has black hair,
She looks like a furry bear.
She likes to play about
And never goes in a pout.

My dog Kyra has brown eyes
And she likes apple pies.
She is only four years old,
But she never gets cold.

My dog Kyra is so funny,
She hates and chases bunnies.
She is black like coal,
Playing football, always scoring a goal.

Danielle Havard (11)
Saron CP School

THE LAZY FROG

In the wood by the town was a bog,
And in it there lived a frog.
The large frog liked to swim all day
And catch the flies that came to play.

One day he entered in a race,
He hoped he'd hop into first place.
In the middle of the race he felt quite hot,
So he went to a puddle to find a cool spot.

He fell asleep under a lily pad,
When he woke up, he was feeling quite sad.
The race was over, another had won,
So he jumped in the pond to have some fun.

Beth Caddell (10)
Saron CP School

PETS

My pets are best,
Better than the rest.
A cat, a rabbit,
With different habits.
Cat likes to jump and pounce,
Rabbit likes to chew and munch,
And I love them both so much.

Sara-Jayne Martin (10)
Saron CP School

SILLY JIMMY

'Silly Jimmy
Where are you?
I've cooked your food,
I've ironed your clothes,
What else do you want me to do?

Silly Jimmy,
Your friends are here,
What shall I say?
Shall I say go away?
What else shall I do?

Silly Jimmy,
I've tried my best,
I'm shouting here and there.
Stop jumping on your bed.
What else are you going to do?'

Tiffany Anderson (11)
Saron CP School

A FRIEND

A friend that comes,
A friend that goes,
So many people,
But one I chose.

This friend is special,
He looks at me,
Then I look back
And always see

Eyes so blue
And freckles so free,
His hair is brown.
And always a smile,
Never have I seen a frown.

So now you know,
My friend so good
Never an argument,
Or a word misunderstood.
So at the end of the day,
I'll just say
I've go a friend,
Haven't you?

Joseph Watkeys (9)
Swiss Valley Primary School

AT THE BEACH

I love the beach in summertime.
Golden sand trickles through my toes,
The shimmering sun sparkles on the sea.
I close my eyes and listen to the waves,
Gently foaming on the shore.
Happy children having lots of fun,
The seaside donkeys having a run.
As I run into the cool water,
A little dog went splashing by.
The salty water touches my lips.

In wintertime, the beach looks bare.
Giant waves crash across the rocks,
Little pebbles scatter like peas.
The cold, grey sky looks very glum,
There's just no sign of any sun.
It's just like sitting on an empty island,
I shiver and pull my scarf around me.
Time to go home, it's getting late,
I pick up a shell and tuck it away
As a reminder of that cold, damp day.

Helen Vessey (10)
Swiss Valley Primary School

HOCUS-POCUS

Hocus-pocus turn around, up and down it makes a sound.
Spotted bat, plenty of gnats, mangled cats and rotten rats.
Add a dog and squash it flat.
Watch the brew bubble and spit, it's nearly ready, no time to sit.
Add the brain of a crazy moose, some slimy worms
To add some juice.
It's nearly done, few things to add to make it taste really bad.
The ears of a mouse and a beak of a bird,
Oh my gosh, it looks absurd.
Hocus-pocus turn around, up and down it makes a sound.
Blop it's done.

Chelsey Forey (11)
Ysgol Y Castell

THE WITCH'S SPELL

Mixture bubble, spit and splatter,
Round the pot we pitter-patter.

Guts of slug, all mashed up,
Eyeballs from a little pup,
Eye of sheep and prey of hawk,
Yolk of egg and a dog's bark,
Heart of hart and shepherd's crook,
Watch them boil and take a look.
Round the black cauldron spit and spew,
Stir it well so it turns to goo.

Mixture bubble, spit and splatter,
Round the pot we pitter-patter.

Andrew Peebles (11)
Ysgol Y Castell

DOUBLE TROUBLE

Bubble, bubble, pop and spit,
Make me a potion
Now the fire is lit.

Lizard's tail and brain of brat,
Tail of rat and whiskers of cat.
Bubble, bubble, pop and spit,
Make me a potion
Now the fire is lit.
Intestines of dog and rhino's poo,
Muscle and fat, skin of rhino too.
Heart of cat and jellybaby sweets,
And rhubarb tart,
Bubble, bubble, pot and spit,
Make me a potion
Now the fire is lit.

Daniel Williams (11)
Ysgol Y Castell

THE DESERTED CITY

Gloomy houses close their sleepy eyes,
Dark, mystical clouds roar
With hunger,
Their raindrops heavy.
Deep drains waiting, waiting,
The large lamp post shivered
In the twilight.
Smelly dustbin laughs the
Last of the sun away.

Elisabeth Collyer (11)
Ysgol Y Castell

HOCUS-POCUS

Round the cauldron we laugh and dance,
Throw in herbs while we sing and prance.

Blood of snake, ugly frogs' legs,
Tail of lamb, old wooden pegs.
Hoof of a donkey, eye of a snake,
Into the pot, watch them bake.
Beak of duck and ducklings' wings,
Tooth of whale and old shark fins.
Bring us children to give flavour,
That will teach them for poor behaviour.

Rachel George (11)
Ysgol Y Castell

EMPTY STREETS

Short hunched school
Dances,
Old battered chimneys
Sit around all day,
Empty houses cry,
Dry satellite dishes die,
Hungry bin
Chases a packet of
Cheese and onion crisps.

Paul Gravell (11)
Ysgol Y Castell

THE STREET

On the road
Tall houses blow,
Passing cars laugh
As they shout their warning.
Rustling ginger leaves perish,
Grass complains and
Takes up its sword.
Rusty, dirty drains smirk.

Laura Sugden (10)
Ysgol Y Castell

WITCHES' CHANT

Hocus-pocus around we go,
Stir and simmer nice and slow.

Croak of frog and howl of dog,
Brain of bird, splinter of log,
A teacher's shout, loud and strong,
Blast of thunder and King Kong.
The guts of brats smashed like ants,
Witches' chant and underpants,
A starfish leg to give it spice,
Whiskers of cat, bucket of lice.

Hocus-pocus around we go,
Stir and simmer nice and slow.

Natalie Harding (10)
Ysgol Y Castell

The Witches' Spell

Abracadabra we like trouble,
Mixture crumble, boil and bubble.

Brain of rat, cats so smelly,
Snake's belly, stinking wellies.
Shadow of death, claws of bear,
Hogwarts' steam, children beware!
Throw all in and watch them boil,
Flavour with mud and old, dry soil.
Chuckie doll and leg of frog.

Abracadabra we like trouble,
Mixture crumble, boil and bubble.

Kieran Edwards (11)
Ysgol Y Castell

STILL DESERTED STREET

Grumpy, sly aerial
Scowls sourly at the hooting owl,
While posh satellite dishes
Stare superiorly.
Tooting, angry car plods by,
Muttering to himself,
Street light sulks,
Mad, munching bin chews
On a rotten apple core,
While a drunken wine bottle
Bounces down the road.
Sneaky, sly signs
Lead to the wrong way,
Silently . . .

Joshua Lowe (10)
Ysgol Y Castell

TROUBLE STREET

The headlights stare.
Slithery snake cars go by,
Street lights unsheathe their teeth to the road,
Stormclouds cover the sky,
Leaves and trees dance in the wind,
Motorbikes grumble,
Gates grind their teeth together,
Back doors shut up
And keep out the night.

Craig Hartland (10)
Ysgol Y Castell

THE WITCHES' SPELL

Bubble, froth, sizzle, snazzle,
Fire blaze and potion dazzle.

Rotten guts of smelly snake,
Lungs of child who's stuffed with cake,
Egg of cuckoo wrapped in poo,
Wizards' warts covered in glue,
Heart of whale and nose of dog,
Crunchy cockroach and dead squid,
Skin of shark, well behaved kid,
Croak of frog and howl of dog.

Bubble, froth, sizzle, snazzle,
Fire blaze and potion dazzle.

Joshua Luke Nicholas (10)
Ysgol Y Castell

EARLY MORNING STREET

Down dull street,
Slow old van jerks along,
Tired wipers waving sleepily,
Dim street lights blink their last winks,
A broken gate screeches,
Scared satellite screams,
Scruffy, skinny aerial scowls at the dawn chorus,
Mad, munching bin
Starts to gobble its breakfast
Greedily!

Natalie Eckley (10)
Ysgol Y Castell

THE HAUNTED STREET

Cable cried for help.
In the garden,
The smelly slimy greenhouse
Smashed.
Big fat chimney,
Smokes.
At the roadside,
Smelly bin munches
More and more and more.

Rhona Rahman (10)
Ysgol Y Castell

HOUSE ON HAUNTED HILL

Empty ghostly house
Threatens . . .
Frightened shed recoils,
Old rusty letterbox slams
And shuts up,
Phone box, happy and excited,
Shouts out to be answered.
Grasshopper car hops by
Along the cracked tarmac road.

Nathan Jones (11)
Ysgol Y Castell

ELEPHANTS

The ground shudders and trumpets sound,
As the big, grey giants roam around.
Huge, loose ears like symbols clap,
While they wander through their annual map.
All the same, young and old,
Creatures gentle, so I'm told.
Skin like leather - smooth and wrinkled,
Small, dark eyes which pierce or twinkle.
Bearing tusks curved and strong
Of ivory - they grow so long.
Majestic, dignified, full of grace,
Tree trunk legs moving at a leisurely pace.
By far the biggest yet,
Like the mammoth old, it gains respect.
Beware! If you should ever meet one, no regrets,
For they say an elephant never forgets!

Bethan Pritchard (10)
Ysgol Y Fro

MINERVA THE CAT

Minerva the cat
Used to catch lots of rats
And sit on the mat
All day.

While out late one night,
She had a great fright,
For a new cat on the block
She did see.

She followed the cat
Deep into the forest,
Until it sat
And stared . . .

The cat was white
And small,
With eyes as bright
As stars.

Suddenly it was gone,
Just like that.
She didn't know how it was done,
Oh how she wished she was back on her mat!

And suddenly she was back
In her house,
And sitting beside her
Was her favourite toy mouse!

Anna Bowen (9)
Ysgol Y Fro

ALIEN

I once saw an alien,
His skin was minty green,
His eyes were fiery red.
I ran around the building but he followed me.
Behind him, he left a slimy green trail.
I ran like the wind but he caught me,
I didn't know what to do.
He took me into his spaceship,
The spaceship was covered in slime.
The alien took to the control panel,
There were a lot of buttons there.
I didn't know what the alien wanted with me,
But I hope he lets me go home by bedtime.

Rhiannon Lewis (9)
Ysgol Gynradd Cwmgors

THE STARRY SKY

Stars in the sky,
Ever so bright,
Sparkling like diamonds
In the night.

The moon is shining
And Arran white,
Glowing like a light bulb
All through the night.

The sky is graphite black
And the stars are twinkling.
The moon is like a banana
All night long.

As dawn strikes,
The sun rises
And glows like a yellow spark.

Alex Horanszky (8)
Ysgol Gynradd Cwmgors

ICE MONSTER

There's an ice monster in my fridge,
I once saw him on a ridge.
With that cold stare,
He gave me quite a scare.

He's always eating my candy
And drinking my dad's brandy.
He's such a pain,
I could hit him with a cane.

He eats the fish
Right out of the dish.
He *bangs* and *bangs* at the fridge door,
I don't want him here anymore.

Jason Locke (10)
Ysgol Gynradd Cwmgors

MY HIDDEN TREASURE

One icy cold evening with a treacherous wind howling,
I hear a deafening eruption.
While peering out into the night,
A dazzling light shone into my eyes.
The golden swirl of stars,
The cold breeze,
The icy blue sky,
All of this was described as treasure night.
Suddenly, an Arran-coloured chest fell from a hatch in
the ceiling.
Inside was a mini portal to Heaven.
The portal was wonderful,
Swirling around, and black.
I stepped inside and saw the amazing colours.
I thought I was not ready for it, but I was.
That portal was my very own hidden treasure.

Joshua Butler-Woolcock (9)
Ysgol Gynradd Cwmgors

RED KITE

Red kite flies through the sky
As its red feathers catch my eye.
Scanning the fields for his lunch,
As a mouse pops out, he swoops down
And back up with his feed.
He's soaring through the sky,
Waiting for day to pass by.
Diving down for a drink,
And gliding over me as I think.
Quietly he sits on the ground,
Recovering from his labours
And then quickly shoots back to his nest
As night falls.

Justin Owen (9)
Ysgol Gynradd Cwmgors

POLAR BEAR

Polar bear with your eyes so blue,
You like me and I like you.
He's nice and fluffy,
His hair is scruffy,
He likes to run,
He think it's fun.
He is so bored,
I can't afford
To keep him around,
Unless he does not make a sound.
I found him in a ditch
On a white snow pitch
In the North Pole,
Eating a mole,
Exploring the world around him.
He's big and nice,
He eats all the rice.
At the end of the day,
He wants to play,
But I like him anyway.

Ethan Price (11)
Ysgol Gynradd Cwmgors